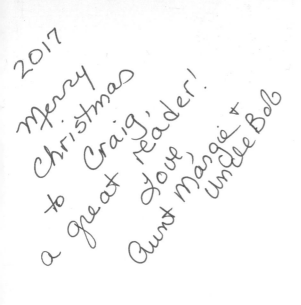

2017

Merry
Christmas
to Craig,
a great reader!
Love,
Aunt Margie +
Uncle Bob

A SYD HOFF
STORY COLLECTION

Stories and Pictures by
Syd Hoff

HARPER

An Imprint of HarperCollinsPublishers

Contents:

STANLEY

STANLEY

A long time ago there were no houses
and people lived in caves.

Stanley lived in a cave,

but he did not like it.

The cave was cold.

So Stanley was cold.

His head hurt because

he had to sleep with it on a rock.

Bats flew around as though

they owned the place.

13

"Why can't we find

a better way to live?"

asked Stanley.

"This is good enough for us,"

said the other cavemen.

"Why isn't it good enough for you?"

The cavemen carried clubs.

They were very tough.

Stanley was tough, too.

17

But he liked to plant seeds

in the ground

and watch them grow.

He liked to paint pictures.

He liked to be nice to people.

He was kind to animals.

The other cavemen did not
want Stanley to act this way.
"Can't you act more like a
caveman?" they asked.

Stanley did not answer.

He went on planting seeds

and painting pictures.

He went on being kind to animals

and nice to people.

He even started saying things like
"Please," and "Thank you,"
and "Lovely day today, isn't it?"

This made the other cavemen
very angry.

"You can't live here," they said.

"Beat it!"

They threw rocks at Stanley

and chased him away.

"We're sorry you lost your cave,"

said the animals.

"I don't care," said Stanley.

"It was cold anyway."

28

He looked for a place to live.

"You can't live in a nest,"
said the birds.

"You can't live in the water,"
said the fish.

30

"You can't live in the ground,"
said a worm.

"Maybe I can live in a tree,"

said Stanley.

"Not while I'm up here,"

said an ape.

"Maybe I can live in space,"

said Stanley.

He jumped off a rock.

"Ouch!" said Stanley.

"I can't live in space!"

Stanley saw a field.

"Does anybody mind if I live here?"

he asked.

"I don't mind if you don't snore,"

said an animal

who was going to sleep.

"I don't mind if you don't

eat too much grass,"

said an animal who was eating.

38

"I don't mind
if you don't take up
too much room,"
said a very,
very big animal.

Stanley made himself at home.

"This is not bad," he said.

But suddenly the wind blew

and Stanley was cold.

The rain fell and he was wet.

41

"This is worse than the cave,"

said Stanley.

He made walls

to keep out the wind.

He made a roof

to keep out the rain.

43

He made a door,

windows and chimney.

He made a house!

"That's the first house I ever saw,"
said a field mouse.

45

"It's the first one I ever made,"
said Stanley.

"Won't you stay here
and live with me?"

"I can't. I belong in the field.
But I will come and visit you
from time to time,"
said the field mouse.

47

Stanley painted pictures.

48

He planted seeds in the ground
and watched them grow.

He loved his house.

But he was lonesome.

"I wonder how my friends are,"

he said.

The cavemen were out

hunting for animals.

They carried their clubs.

51

"Look who's after us

with their silly clubs,"

said the animals.

"Let's chase them out of here!"

They chased the cavemen.

Stanley saw the cavemen running.

"Don't be afraid," he said.

"I won't let them hurt you."

He made the animals go away.

"You saved us, Stanley,"
said the cavemen.
"Thank you."

56

"Come back and live in our cave,"
said one caveman.

"Caves are old-fashioned," said Stanley.

"Come and see where I live."

He showed them his house.

"A cave is for bears.

A house is for people,"

said Stanley.

"You are right, Stanley,"

said the cavemen.

"This is the way we want to live."

They all made houses.

Stanley showed them
how to paint pictures
and plant seeds.

He showed them

how to be nice to each other

and kind to animals,

and everybody was happy.

OLIVER

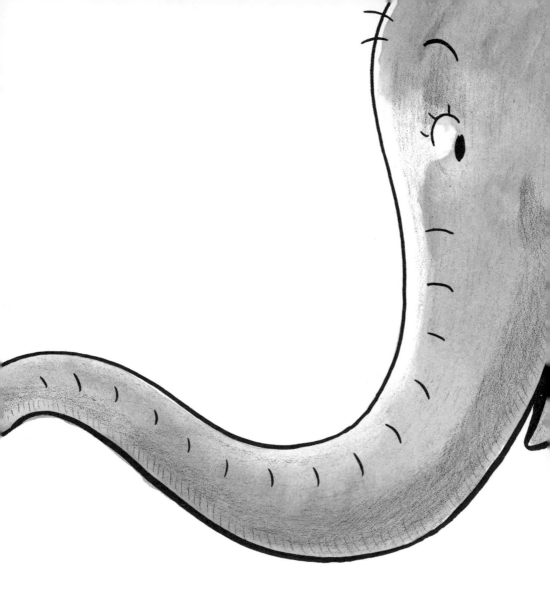

Some elephants came across the ocean

on a ship.

They were going to work in the circus.

One elephant's name was Oliver.

When they landed

the circus man counted them:

"One, two, three, four, five,

six, seven, eight, nine, ten elephants."

"And one makes eleven," said Oliver.

"There must be a mistake.

I ordered only ten elephants,"

said the circus man.

"We don't need eleven."

75

"I won't take up much room,"

said Oliver.

"Elephants always do,"

said the circus man.

76

"Good-bye, Oliver,"

said the other elephants.

"Take good care of yourself."

Oliver was all alone.

He didn't know where to go.

A little mouse came along.

"Why don't you try the zoo?"

said the mouse.

"You look like the type they use there."

"Thanks, I'll go at once," said Oliver.

"Taxi!" said Oliver.

"What you need is a moving van,"

said the taxi man.

He did not stop.

Oliver followed the cars.

The drivers held out their hands

when they made a turn.

When Oliver made a turn

he held out his trunk.

He saw a woman weighing herself.

"My goodness,

I'm as heavy as an elephant," she said.

Oliver got on the scale.

"I'm heavy as an elephant, too,"

he said.

At last Oliver reached the zoo.

"Who is in charge here?" he asked.

"I am," said a man.

"Do you need an elephant?" asked Oliver.

"I'm sorry, not right now,"

said the zoo man.

"Thanks anyway," Oliver said

and walked away.

A man was selling peanuts.

"May I help you sell them?" asked Oliver.

"Would you sell them or eat them?"

asked the man.

"Eat them," said Oliver.

The man gave him some peanuts

for being honest.

Oliver left the zoo.

He walked down the street.

"Would anyone like to have me for a pet?"

he asked.

"I have a parakeet," said one person.

"I have goldfish," said another person.

"I have a cat," said another person.

"I have a duck," said someone else.

"I'd like a dog for a pet," said a lady.

"I can pretend I'm a dog," said Oliver.

"All right," she said.

Oliver and the lady went for a walk.

"Bowwow," said Oliver.

"What a nice dog," said the people.

"He's the biggest dog we ever saw!"

"I am hungry," said Oliver.

"Let's go home."

"Don't you have any hay?" he asked.

"No, but I have a nice bone,"

said the lady.

"Elephants need hay," Oliver said.

"I guess I can't be your dog after all.

But thank you, and good-bye."

"Good-bye," said the lady.

Oliver walked and walked.

Some people were riding horses.

Oliver watched.

"Horses get hay.

I wish I were a horse," he said.

"Do you need a horse?" asked Oliver.

"You look like an elephant.

But I'll ride you," said a man.

The man sat on Oliver's back.

"Giddyap," he said.

The horses jumped over the fence.

Plop!

Oliver could not jump over the fence.

"I guess I'm not a horse," he said.

"Good-bye."

"Good-bye," said the man.

Oliver passed a playground.

"May I play?" hc asked.

"You may swing us," said the children.

"Is this the way?" asked Oliver.

"Not quite," said the children.

"But it will do."

"How does this work?" asked Oliver.

"It's a seesaw.

We'll get on the other side,"

said the children.

"Well?" asked Oliver.

The children rushed for the slide.

They couldn't all get on at once.

Oliver helped out.

It was time to rest.

The children talked about

what they wanted to be

when they grew up.

"I want to be a policeman," said Tommy.

"I want to be a nurse," said Mary.

"I want to be a cowboy," said Ben.

"I always wanted to work in the circus,"

said Oliver.

"I could be a dancing elephant."

He started to dance for the children.

Everybody stopped to watch.

They didn't see the circus parade coming.

They all watched Oliver.

They didn't see the acrobats.

They didn't see the jugglers.

They didn't see the clowns!

'Are they looking at me?"

asked the lion tamer.

'No," said the lion.

'They're looking at some elephant dancing."

121

"What's going on here?"

said the circus owner.

He ran over to look.

"That's the best dancing elephant
I've ever seen," he said.

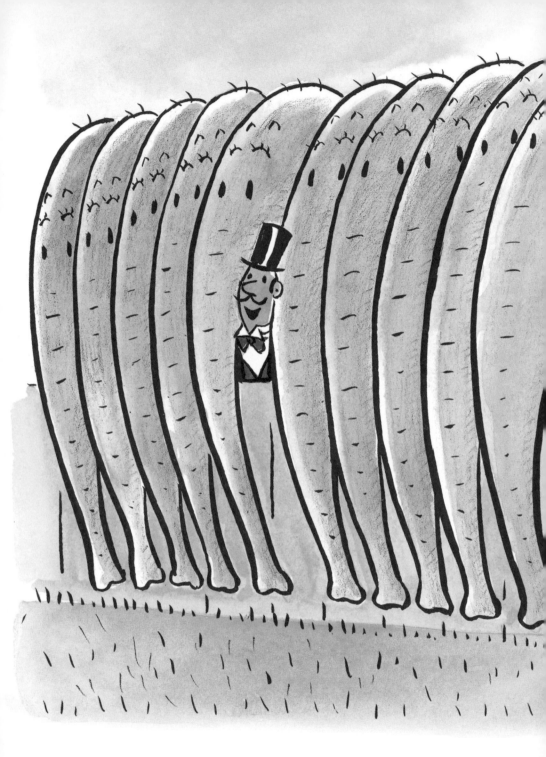

"It's Oliver!" cried the other elephants.

"Oliver," said the circus man,

"I made a big mistake. We do need you.

Will you join the circus?"

125

"I'd love to," said Oliver.

"Hurray," cried the children.

"You got your wish!"

"Will you remember us?"

asked the children.

"Of course," said Oliver.

"An elephant never forgets."

"And even a rhinoceros

would remember the fun we had."

Sammy
THE SEAL

Sammy
THE SEAL

It was feeding time at the zoo.

All the animals

were getting their food.

The lions ate their meat.

The elephants ate their hay.

The monkeys ate their bananas.

The bears ate their honey.

Then it was time

for the seals to be fed.

Mr. Johnson took them fish.

"Hooray for fish!" said the seals.

They jumped in the water.

Soon the basket was empty.

"That is all there is," said Mr. Johnson.

"There is no more."

"Thank you for the fish," said the seals.

"They were good."

The seals were happy.

But one little seal was not happy.

He sat by himself.

He looked sad.

"What is wrong, Sammy?"

said Mr. Johnson.

144

"I want to know
what it is like
outside the zoo," said the little seal.
"I want to go out and look around."

"All right, Sammy," said Mr. Johnson.

"You have been a good seal.

You may go out and see."

"Good-bye, Sammy," said the other seals.

"Have a good time."

"Good-bye," said Sammy.

"Where are you going?" said the zebra.

"I am going out," said Sammy.

"Have fun," said the hippo.

"Come back soon," said the giraffe.

Sammy walked and walked and walked.

He did not know what to look at first.

"That seal must be from out of town,"
said a man.

Sammy looked at everything.

"What street is this?" said a man.

"I am a stranger here myself,"

said Sammy.

"I guess it is feeding time here, too,"
said Sammy.

"That is a lovely fur coat," said a lady.

"Where did you get it?"

"I was born with it," said Sammy.

"I wish I could find some water.

I am hot. I want to go swimming,"

said Sammy.

"We are sorry. There is no room for you
in this puddle," said the birds.

"And there is no room for you here," said the goldfish.

"Keep out," said the policeman.

"You cannot swim in there."

"Ah, here is a place!" said Sammy.

"Who is in my bathtub?" said someone.

"I am sorry," said Sammy.

He left at once.

Some children were standing in line.

Sammy got in line, too.

"What are we waiting for?"

asked Sammy.

"School. What do you think?" said a boy.

"That will be fun.

I will come, too," Sammy said.

The teacher was not looking.

Sammy sat down.

The children made words with blocks.

Sammy wished he could spell.

"All right, children.

Now we will all sing a song,"

said the teacher.

The children had good voices.

"That sounds fine," said the teacher.

"But one of you is barking—

just like a seal."

"Is it you, Joey?"

said the teacher.

"No," said Joey.

"Is it you, Helen?"

said the teacher.

"No," said Helen.

"Is it you, Dorothy, Robert,

Fred, Joan, or Agnes?"

"No," said the children.

"Then it must be you,"
said the teacher.

"I am sorry. This school is
just for boys and girls."

"Please let me stay," said Sammy.

"I will be good."

"All right. You may stay,"

said the teacher.

Sammy was happy.

He sat at his desk

and looked at the teacher.

He learned how to read.

He learned how to write.

"And now it is time to play,"
said the teacher.

"Who wants to play a game?"

"We do," said the children.

They threw the ball over the net.

"The ball must not hit the ground,"
cried Sammy's team.

"Somebody catch the ball."

Sammy caught the ball on his nose!

A boy on the other team tried
to catch the ball on his nose, too.
"Boys must catch with their hands,"
said the teacher.

Sammy tried to catch the ball
with his flippers.

"Seals must catch with their noses,"
said the teacher.

Up and down went the ball,

from one side to the other.

At last the teacher blew her whistle.

"Who wins?" said the children.

"It is even," said the teacher.

Everybody was happy.

A bell rang. School was over.

"Will you be here tomorrow?"

said the children.

"No," said Sammy.

"School is fun,

but I belong in the zoo.

I just wanted to know

what it is like outside.

Now I have to go back."

"Good-bye, Sammy," said the children.

"We will come to see you."

"Good," said Sammy.

Sammy was in a hurry

to get back to the zoo.

He had so much to tell the other seals.

"May I welcome you home, Sammy,"
said Mr. Johnson.
"I am glad you are back.
You are just in time for dinner."

"There's no place like home,"
said Sammy.